NORAH'S
NASTY KNICKERS

NORAH'S NASTY KNICKERS

Crazy Poems for Cool Kids

by
Gez Walsh

Illustrated by the author

The King's England Press
2002

ISBN 1 872438 80 6

Norah's Nasty Knickers is typeset by Moose Manuscripts
in Times New Roman 14pt and published by
The King's England Press,
Cambertown House, Commercial Road, Goldthorpe,
Rotherham, South Yorkshire, S63 9BL

Printed and bound in Great Britain by:

Woolnough Bookbinding
Irthlingborough
Northamptonshire

Foreword

I would like to say that if you buy this book you would become very rich, meet the person of your dreams and travel the world.

I would like to say all these things, but I can't, because my publishing company says that they are just lies and a cheap attempt by me to get you to buy a book.

My publishers say that I have to stick to the truth which is, if you buy this book, you will read about lots of strange characters and have a good laugh.

And who knows. One day you might become rich and meet the person of your dreams and travel the world!

Dedication

This book is dedicated to all the staff and pupils of all the schools that I have visited. Thank you all for your support.

Norah's Nasty Knickers

Norah had some knickers
That were not very good -
A witch gave them to her
While out walking in the wood.

Norah was usually a good girl
With an attitude so mild,
But when she wore the knickers
She became a horrible little child.

The witch had cast a spell,
With lots of cackles and sniggers,
And turned a pair of ordinary pants
Into a pair of nasty knickers.

They made Norah swear,
And often started fights;
The knickers just laughed
Beneath Norah's school tights.

Norah's mum had noticed the change,
The moans and the bickers.
She said, "I've seen this magic before -
She's wearing nasty knickers!"

The knickers soon realised
Norah's mum was on their case,
So they escaped from the wash-basket
That night with great haste.

When she saw the knickers next, on T.V.,
Norah let out such a cry:
"That woman's wearing my nasty knickers!"
As she said, "You are the weakest link - goodbye!"

Superhero Friends

Let me introduce some superheroes,
Of none you will have heard.
That's because their super powers
Are all useless and quite absurd.

First there is the Cowpat Man
Who lies low in a field unseen.
He's flat and very smelly
And a very strange shade of green.

Super villains will never see him
Until they slip upon his back;
He then jumps all over them
With his super cowpat splat.

The next one is just as odd,
Nettle Man, who can be quite brash;
If the villains have a brush with him
They come out in a nasty rash.

And finally there's Pen Man
Who is old and rather quaint;
When he's angered by villains
He writes them a letter of complaint.

I hope you liked those heroes,
In comics they will never be hits.
I am the hero Spot Man -
I scare people to death with my zits!

The Prayer of a Bad Boy

Every night I go to sleep
I pray my new teacher's not a creep.
I hope my old teacher doesn't come back
Or ever find out that I got her the sack.

I pray my pet snake will be found soon
After escaping in my mum's bedroom.
I pray my sister doesn't have a rage
Because I opened the door on her hamster's cage.

I pray that my mum doesn't feel any stress
When she sees the kite made from her new dress.
I hope that Grandad has a sense of humour
When he finds his false teeth stuck up the Hoover.

And so I end my nightly prayer:
Make my Headmaster work elsewhere.
Please watch over me, I think you should,
Because just of late I've been quite good.

A Gift of Love

I loved a girl named Emma,
She really was quite nice.
I gave her my heart forever,
She gave me her head lice!

Sleepy Dirt

Every night I go to sleep
I shut my eyes without a peep.
When I awake with such surprise
I have little bogies in my eyes.

Where are they from do you suppose?
Have they escaped from inside my nose?
A bogey in the eye is very scary -
Was it brought by a bogey fairy?

All these thoughts inside my head,
"Not to worry," my mother said.
It's only natural and it doesn't hurt,
It's the body's way of clearing sleepy dirt.

Kelly and O'Keefe

This is a very long story
But I will try to keep it brief,
It's about two old men
Named Kelly and O'Keefe.

They were building a house,
Just fitting up a ceiling
When the house it shook,
Both had a bad feeling.

They looked at each other,
Kelly said, "What's that din?"
Both ran for the door
As the ceiling fell in.

Under rubble they laid
Not knowing what to do.
"Are you alive?" asked Kelly
"Yes," replied O'Keefe. "Are you?"

On scrambling from the mess
Kelly stared at O'Keefe
Who was feeling his mouth
Saying, "I've losht mi teef!"

On dusting themselves down
They had a look around;
Through timber and plaster
O'Keefe's teeth couldn't be found.

O'Keefe was very worried.
"I can't go home like thish-
My wife doesn't know I've no teef-
What if she wants a kish?"

So he packed up his tools,
His saws and his wrenches,
Then Kelly saw, as O'Keefe bent down,
That stuck to his bum were his dentures.

Kelly laughed and then shouted,
"O'Keefe, my old son!
I know where your teeth are!
They're biting your own bum!"

I Can Only See the Sea

They say to put a shell to your ear
To hear the sea for a minute,
But I couldn't with one I found
Because it still had a cockle in it!

Seeing the Light!

Herbert was a young caterpillar
Who hid under a big dock leaf,
Eating his way day and night
Because a caterpillar's life is brief.

Soon Herbert became a pupa,
Just hanging in the shade,
Waiting for a special event
A transformation to be made.

Herbert climbed from his cocoon,
Drying his wings in the breeze.
He took a puzzled look at them
And said, "What the heck are these?"

Herbert is now a big moth
Who comes out late at night,
And spends the rest of his life
Banging his head on our kitchen light!

Big Daddy

My father is a big, big man
From his head you could abseil;
When he strips to have a swim
He looks rather like a whale.

When he jumps in the pool
You have to be quite brave
As small children disappear
On a giant tidal wave.

People will always run
When he turns up for a swim;
The sports centre ends up flooded
And it's all because of him.

Sharp-Shooting Shirley

Shirley was quite a small dog,
She wouldn't grow much bigger.
They say that she's a gun dog,
But I can't find her trigger!

Saying Something Stupid

People say the strangest things
That always make me groan:
When I asked my mum what she was doing
She replied, "I'm on the phone."

Now sitting on a telephone
Is a very strange thing to do,
But mum's friend, Pat, is worse -
She asked to borrow our loo!

Where on earth would she take it?
It's smelly and full of dregs;
Then grandma said something stupid,
That she'd been to hospital with her legs!

Why don't people speak properly?
Or don't bother to speak at all.
I would never say such stupid things -
They're all driving me up the wall!

Strange Sale

A woman stopped grandad in the street,
She did this to people by habit
Asking would he like a lucky rabbit's foot.
"No" he replied, "it wasn't lucky for the rabbit."

Strange Fellow

Little Henry Mellow
Was a very strange fellow
Who lived down our street.
He'd stick out his tongue
And show his bum
To everyone that he'd meet.

Ronnie's Little Monster

Little Ronnie Wright
Had a monster in his room,
Jumping on his bed,
Singing out of tune.

Dancing and singing
With pants on its head,
Tipping out his drawers,
Hiding food under the bed.

Ronnie's mum would scream,
Each and every night,
Because the monster in his room
Was little Ronnie Wright.

P... Perishing P... Penguins

Who designed the penguins?
Their brains must have been numb,
Making a creature that lives on ice
And has to drag around its bum.

For flying their wings are useless,
They're for swimming, we're told;
No wonder they look surprised,
That water is far too cold.

They should have had big wings
And be covered with fur and hair;
If you keep them as they are
At least move them elsewhere.

The ice pack's not a place
For penguins to meet
When their bums are on the ground
And they have nothing on their feet.

King Kong Clive

Give a big warm welcome
To the funniest man alive -
He travels with the circus
And they call him King Kong Clive.

He's six feet ten,
Weighs twenty-two stone
And when he walks on stage
People start to groan.

He can juggle six beer crates
With just one hand
While using the other
To conduct the band.

He performs useless tricks
That always go wrong
And to finish his act
He sings a stupid song.

But people always laugh
As he squirts water from a rose,
Because if they don't
He punches them on the nose.

Teacher Talk

"Right then, good morning class five.
Fiona, my dear, please sit up straight
And Paul take your hands from your pants
And would you please try to concentrate!"

"Oh, what is wrong now, Timothy?
Yes, go on then, hurry to the toilet,
I don't want your mum here again
Complaining your trousers were wet."

"Charlotte, take your finger from your nose.
Jason, dear, are you not feeling well?
Yes, Kyle, I do know it's him
Making that terrible smell."

"Right, now could we do the register?
Adam. Adam! Is Adam Aston here?
No, Leanne, he has diarrhoea
Not the squits my dear."

"Right, is there anyone else missing?
Who was that called out 'yes'?
Kevin, I should have known it was you,
And Barry, stop looking down Mary's dress."

"You're the same every Monday morning,
You come in and scream and shout;
I'm off to the staff room for a coffee -
You lot can sort yourselves out!"

20

Miguel the Nasty Gnat

Miguel the mad mosquito
Causes people so much pain,
He preys on holidaymakers
On the coast of sunny Spain.

Every night in hotel rooms
Lie bodies so lard-white;
Miguel sees them a mile off
And pops in for a quick bite.

Miguel feasts on foreign blood
Leaving his victims aching;
Next morning they awake scratching,
Looking like a side of bacon.

People will use sprays and gels
To take nasty Miguel to task,
But they don't bother him,
He just wears a gas mask.

So if you go to Spain this year
You must remember to take care,
Because in the corner of your room
Miguel will be waiting there.

Dimbo Himbo

Six foot six
With a chiselled chin,
Perfect good looks
But rather dim.

He's a dimbo himbo.

He started as a lumberjack
Chopping up big logs,
Moved on to modelling clothes
In glossy catalogues.

He's a dimbo himbo.

Then came the film roles,
All in rather bad taste,
Killing all the bad guys
With his hair still in place.

He's a dimbo himbo.

Women always love him,
He always loves them;
It's strange that all his fans
Seem to be men.

He's a dimbo himbo.

He's a man of many projects,
All for a good cause;
He'd like to save the world
If he knew where it was.

He's a dimbo himbo.

His face is on many posters
All over town,
So until the next dimbo himbo
He's the superhero clown.

The Vampire Party

The vampires threw a party
For everyone they knew
So the locals stocked up on garlic
And on crucifixes, too.

They sent out lots of invites
To all the ghouls and cranks,
Then they made lots of withdrawals
From the local blood banks.

Soon the big night arrived,
The party was in full swing;
Mrs. Dracula kissed her husband
Then she bit him on the chin.

Igor had never been so excited
As he started to dance and jitter.
He said, "Master, I'm happy.
Even my back feels better."

A vampire dated the mummy,
His cold heart full of lust;
He bit the mummy on the neck
And got a mouthful of dust.

Everyone was so happy,
All screaming and bawling
No one had noticed the time -
It was nearly morning.

As the cockerel called
Sunlight filled the hall,
The vampires turned to dust
As they started to fall.

The hall was soon empty,
Igor stood in a deathly hush;
Smouldering ash covered the floor.
Said Igor, "I'll get my brush."

The locals are now happy
As their garlic they can dump;
Igor's all alone in the castle,
They say he has the hump.

Soldier Jim

Jimmy was made a soldier,
They gave him a big gun
But whenever he saw fighting,
Jimmy would always run.

People said he was a coward
Because he wanted war to cease;
He didn't believe in killing,
Jimmy only believed in peace.

They said he should be a hero
And charge like a fighting bull,
But Jimmy knew about heroes,
They kept the graveyards full.

He's not saying it's wrong,
To fight for freedom and peace,
But if we all thought like Jimmy
Then maybe wars would cease.

Fido's Friends

My dog has some strange pets,
I don't think that they're fun;
He has lots of little worms
And he keeps them up his bum!

The Mighty Pen

The pen is mightier than the sword
Is what my teacher told me today,
But if I only had a pen in battle
I think that I would run away.

Anyone for Tennis?

They say that if you're good at tennis
You could make yourself a packet,
But if you were to ask me
I would say tennis is just a racket.

Cyril the Dancing Centipede

There was once a centipede called Cyril,
Who loved to tap-dance in the street,
But he made one heck of a noise
Tap-dancing with one hundred feet.

He made the other insects angry
Because Cyril would dance at night,
He would imagine he was on Broadway
And dance under the lampost light.

The head insect sent out a message
Saying all the insects should meet,
And with them each bring one slipper
So they could put them on Cyril's feet.

They gathered a heap of slippers
And told young Cyril to put them on;
He jumped up and down with no sound,
These shoes for tap-dancing were wrong.

But Cyril was not at all stupid,
Their tempers he would not ruffle;
He no longer tap-dances under lamplight,
Instead he does the soft-shoe shuffle.

Getting a Bit Flushed

I had to use the toilet,
To do what I must do,
But when I'd finished
There was no paper by the loo.

I was home alone,
Needed toilet roll fetching,
But we kept it downstairs
In a cupboard in the kitchen.

I know, strip the centre roll,
This idea was just fantastic;
It was then that I noticed
That the roll was made of plastic.

I would have to go downstairs so,
Pulling my pants to my knees,
I waddled like a penguin
And could feel a nasty breeze.

When I reached the kitchen
I heard a knock at the door:
A woman was staring at me,
She couldn't believe what she saw.

I just stood there smiling
With my pants around my knees;
She could see my dangly bits
Swinging slightly in the breeze.

I had never been so embarrassed,
I didn't know what to do
So I just put my legs together
Then bounced off like a kangaroo.

I never found out who she was,
She never came back, you see,
But now when I go to the toilet
I always take paper with me.

Arnie

Arnie was a muscular termite,
He lived in the holly wood
But he came from overseas
So his English wasn't that good.

Moving from mound to mound
In each he had a new lady;
He'd spend the night chewing wood,
In the morning say, "Hasta la vista, baby."

Other men termites were so jealous
That all the girl termites liked him,
He was quite thick but hunky,
They were quite bright but thin.

So from the mounds he was expelled,
He wasn't welcome any more,
And if the mounds had had them
Arnie would have been shown the door.

He collected up all his belongings,
Put on his dark glasses and mac,
Then turning at the entrance, stopped,
And shouted, "I'll be back!"

He wandered from mound to mound,
But no one would let him in;
He soon developed a hatred for termites
Especially the ones that were thin.

Arnie swore he would get his revenge
And armed with guns and a nasty garotte
Started blowing up termite mounds,
Yes, poor Arnie had totally lost the plot.

You see no one likes an oddball
For their tastes we cannot cater;
The termites' lack of understanding
Turned Arnie into the 'termite hater'.

The Worst Teacher in the World

My teacher called me a turnip,
He said that I was thick,
If I had a brain I would be dangerous,
And that I make him sick.

When I told mum she got angry
Saying, "What a horrible creature!"
When she calls to see him tomorrow
I wouldn't want to be my teacher.

Big is Beautiful

Sharon was a happy troll
Who lived beneath a bridge,
She loved to try beauty products
Keeping a face pack in her fridge.

People had always feared trolls
Because they were big and hairy,
But Sharon wasn't like that,
She wasn't at all scary.

Using hair-removing cream
She revealed her yellow skin,
But because trolls are so hairy
She needed a five-gallon tin.

Sharon attended the local college
To improve her make-up skill,
But they couldn't improve her looks,
She had a face designed to kill.

You see, even though Sharon was nice
And had a personality so bubbly,
I'm afraid it has to be said
That girl was just butt-ugly.

Sharon looked for work
And soon found a new position;
This scared the locals to death,
She had made a bad decision.

Now when they cross her bridge
The steps they take are tentative
In case they bump into Sharon
Who is an Avon representative.

My Little Pony

Paula was a very poorly pony
Who had a very bad cough,
She sneezed and coughed all night,
Next morning she felt rough.

All the coughing took its toll,
She lost her voice in due course;
She whispered to Sadie her friend
"I'm afraid I'm a little horse." .

Darren is a Genius

Darren can roll his eyes back
And touch his tongue on his nose,
He can fold his ears inside out
And bite the nails on his toes.

Darren is totally brilliant,
Everyone thinks he's so cool;
Why don't they teach me this
Instead of useless lessons at school?!

Stupid Old Teabag

A strange woman called at our house,
She told fortunes by looking in cups of tea;
She told mum she was a medium
But she looked like a large to me.

On her fingers she wore gold rings,
Claimed mum's future she could see,
And she would tell her amazing things.
In exchange for a reasonable fee.

She asked mum her birth sign
Saying it was a lucky new moon;
I know why they call her a fortune-teller -
This was going to cost mum a small fortune.

I don't believe in all this rubbish,
Mum's head must be going quite funny;
I could tell her the near future -
She was going to part with a lot of money.

Bullfighting Benny

Benny was a bullfighter,
As brave as brave could be,
But he was not so brave
Because Benny could hardly see.

The crowed would shout out "Toro!"
Then all throw up their hats;
Benny didn't know what the fuss was,
He thought he was shooing away cats.

Each day he would enter the bullring,
The bulls would show no pity;
Waving his big red cloak
Benny would shout, "Shoo, kitty, kitty!"

The enraged bulls would charge
But by a miracle of chance
Benny would always move out of their way
Never receiving as much as a glance.

Yes, Benny was a matador,
Giving audiences a thrill,
But he thought he worked in pest control
For the local Spanish council.

Talking Sense

One old lady phoned her friend
And said, "Hello, is that you?"
"Yes," replied the other old dear,
"And would that be you, too?"
"Yes, it is. Where are you?"
"Oh, you know, I'm stood here."
"Has anyone phoned you today?"
"Yes, you just did, my dear."
"It is so lovely to speak to you,
I don't get out much any more."
"Oh, my dear, have you been ill?"
"No, I just lost the key to the door."
"I thought you'd have phoned sooner,
I've collected for you a token."
"I'm sorry but I can't phone you
Because this phone is broken."
"Doesn't it work at all, my dear?"
"No, it is completely dead."
"Have you rung the telephone people?"
"I can't, my phone's broken, I just said."
"Well, I'll phone you when your phone's fixed."
"Yes, it would be lovely to talk again."
"Goodbye 'til then my old friend.
And, by the way, what is your name?"

Teachers in Love

Mr. Dirkin fancies Miss Ross,
I saw them kissing after school;
Mr. Dirkin is a real dingbat
But Miss Ross is quite cool.

What does she see in such a prat
With his flares and stupid ties?
She's so lovely with long brown hair
And beautiful big brown eyes.

Miss Ross has just started at our school
And she takes us out to lots of parks
Whereas Mr. Dirkin is head of English,
Is she going out with him for extra marks?

An Eight Foot Meal

We went on holiday to Italy,
I had some octopus to eat;
It was white and rather smelly -
I think that I ate its feet!

Freda the Big Tooth Fairy

Freda was a big tooth fairy
And she wasn't very bright;
She never understood the job
That she had to do each night.

Children hide teeth under pillows,
Everywhere from north to south,
But Freda would fly to a sleeping child
Then give them a smack in the mouth.

She did this to my friend, Craig,
He went to bed a lovely-looking fellow,
But the only tooth he had next morning
Was still tucked underneath his pillow.

So, if you see a child at school
Who tends to be a messy eater,
You'll notice they're missing teeth
Because they've had a visit from Freda.

Are You Lonely Tonight?

Sitting in a lonely room,
In a lonely house
In a lonely town,
In the loneliest county
Of a lonely country,
On the loneliest continent around
Is a lonely person
On the saddest planet
In a far flung galaxy
Who's staring at the stars
And thinking to himself
"Is there anyone as lonely as me?"

My Masterpiece

Im going to write a poem different to all the rest I
know you will enjoy it because its going to be my
best I havent thought of a title just yet or if it will be
funny or sad but when you come to read it I know
that it will drive you mad My friend Debbie says
you wont like my creation because it is impossible
to read she has the cheek to say I don't understand
punctuation

Have You Seen My Dog?

Have you seen my dog?
He has one eye, one ear,
Walks with a bit of a limp
'Cos he was hit by a car last year.

He has bald patches on his fur
And always looks so mucky;
If you see him, give him a shout -
He goes by the name of Lucky.

The Crocodile Blues

There was once a crocodile
Who was never very happy,
He was always very rude
And very often snappy.

If any innocent animal
Swam in his river
He'd just float on by
And have them for his dinner.

So all the animals decided
To have a public meeting,
They didn't tell the crocodile
Who was still busy eating.

They said, "We must get rid,
As soon as we can."
So they pooled together
And hired themselves a hit-man.

The hit-man soon arrived,
An evil looking man;
All the birds flew away
And all the animals ran.

The hit-man found the crocodile
And caught him in a trap;
All the animals cheered
And all the birds gave a flap.

But soon they'd stop cheering
And start singing the blues
Because the hit-man returned
Wearing a pair of crocodile shoes.

He started laying traps
Around all the dens and lairs;
The hit-man was a dealer
In exotic feathers and furs.

The river is now safe,
The animals got their wish,
Not an animal left in sight
Just a river full of fish.

So the moral of this story
Is always keep in good health,
And if you have any problems,
Sort them out yourself!

Messy Monsters

When you go to sleep at night
For a well-earned rest,
Do monsters enter your room
And make such an awful mess?

Throwing around old socks,
Spilling drinks they've tried to pour,
Opening up all your drawers
And throwing CDs on the floor.

Well, this always happens in my room,
The evidence is there to see,
But each morning when I tell my mum
She always says that it was me!

Pet Rescue

There was once an old lady
Whose cat had climbed a tree
So she asked her neighbour,
"Would you get it down for me?"

The neighbour got out his ladders,
He would soon have kitty free,
But that cat climbed further up
And was still stuck up the tree.

Soon a crowd did gather,
Along came the local P.C.;
He gave the trunk a shake
But the cat was still stuck up the tree.

So they phoned for the fire brigade
Who arrived at half past three;
With ladders and nets they tried so hard
But the cat was still stuck up the tree.

The fire brigade phoned for a helicopter
That saves sailors lost at sea;
The helicopter blew away all the leaves
But left the cat stuck up the tree.

So now the old lady,
The neighbour, local P.C.,
The fire brigade and navy
Couldn't get the cat from the tree.

But along came a little girl
Shouting, "Here kitty, come to me!"
Then she put down a plate of cat food
And the cat jumped out of the tree!

Bad Moos

We all went to the local community farm
With Mr. Rogers and Mr. Howe;
We all came back with happy memories,
But Ronnie came back with a cow.

He walked it home through the back fields
Then hid it in his garden shed;
"Dad is in for a big shock tomorrow
When he goes to mow the lawn," Ronnie said.

Screams could be heard the next morning,
From Ronnie's house they came, such a row,
As his dad ran shouting down the road
Chased by one angry cow.

The police found Ronnie's dad high up a tree,
He was shaking and looked so meek;
The farmer came to collect the cow saying,
"That's the third that's been nicked this week."

Ronnie's dad was suffering from severe shock
So he went home to bed to sleep;
Ronnie now regretted that he'd nicked the cow
And thought, "Next time, I'll nick him a sheep!"

Sparky

Sparky was a very odd spider,
The strangest spider you could meet;
He wasn't like other spiders,
Sparky didn't have sticky feet.

Other spiders would climb walls
On the look-out for a snack;
Sparky would climb up on four legs
Then fall down on his back.

Many a day he would dream
Of walking upon the ceiling,
But he was ground-bound
So he would never have that feeling.

Flies would often taunt him
By sticking out their tongues,
Then flying to the ceiling
And flashing him their bums.

Sparky was feeling sad,
He'd never felt so low
Until his mum gave him eight boots
Made with soles of Velcro.

He soon put them on
Then ran up the wall
Eating flies on the way -
In fact, he ate them all!

So he had realised his dream
Of walking on the ceiling,
Eating up the cheeky flies
Amongst the paint that was peeling.

But this story doesn't end happy,
In fact the end is quite bad,
But Sparky had lived out his dream,
So for that we shouldn't be sad.

As he walked across the ceiling,
Trying to sneak up on a fly,
All eight bootlaces snapped -
With eight legs he waved the fly goodbye.

He crashed down to the floor
Landing on his head;
A cockroach doctor took his pulse
Then pronounced poor Sparky dead.

All the flies they rejoiced,
The spiders they prayed, kneeling
To eight tiny Velcro boots
Still stuck to the kitchen ceiling.

My Special Girl

I used to meet my girl
By the cricket pitch wall;
She looked like a man
And was very tall.
She had big muscles,
Her hair was thatched,
But if I sat on her shoulders
I could watch the cricket match.

Look and Listen

"Look, dad, at what I've made!"
Said Sammy, oh so proud.
"I've made a house with my tool kit."
Sammy's dad just laughed out loud.

"Look, dad, at what I've made!
It's a boat for us to sail in."
His dad replied, "It's rubbish son,
Just chuck it in the bin."

"Look, dad, at what I've made!
It's a car for you and me."
"That wouldn't move an inch my son,
You must have a brain the size of a pea."

"Look, dad, I've made a time machine!"
Sammy's dad just looked and sneered.
Then Sammy pushed a button
And his father disappeared.

Rain Stops Play

Oh, I wish that I could make it rain,
I wish that I could have such power.
I would cause every type of rain,
From drizzle to a raging shower.

I would make the crops grow
In all the dry and barren lands,
I would stop all the flooding
With just one clap of my hands.

But my reason for rain control,
The most important reason of all,
Is so when someone mentions cricket
I could cause heavy rain to fall!

The Travelling Barnacle

Barney was a barnacle
Stuck to the bottom of a boat
Travelling all over the world,
It was his only way to float.

His ancestors lived in a small pool
From travelling they were prevented;
Barnacles never roamed the sea
Until ocean liners were invented!

The Price of Love

Mum says that when I grow up
I should marry for love not money,
But she ended up with my dad -
I think she's trying to be funny.

A Lad in a Cave

A man in search of fortune
Wandered alone into a cave;
Soon he found himself lost,
He knew he must be brave.

At every turn he stumbled,
He struggled for all his worth
Down deeper into the darkness
Towards the centre of the earth.

He came across a large chamber
By his now fading torch light
And sat with tears in his eyes
At his foolish, desperate plight.

Then something caught his eye
In the chamber so cold and damp;
It was a very strange looking object
Which turned out to be an old oil lamp.

He picked it up and rubbed it clean.
It erupted with a mighty flash -
There appeared a strange looking man
With a turban and a long thin moustache.

The man screamed with terror
Saying, "This just cannot be!"
The stranger replied, "I'm a genie,
And you have just set me free."

"You are now my new master
And I must grant you three wishes,
But hurry up and make it quick
I've to get back to washing the dishes."

The greed light lit in the man's head
As he thought of plots and schemes;
He'd always wanted fame and riches,
Now he could have them beyond his dreams.

"First I wish that in my bank account
You will place one hundred billion pounds.
My next wish is to be world famous,
The sort of fame that knows no bounds."

"My third and last wish is for a woman
So beautiful and she's my loving wife;
When you have granted me these things
I will live a full and wonderful life."

The genie shook his head and smiled,
He'd heard these wishes many times before.
He granted them with a clap of his hands
And thought the man was a total bore.

The lamp and the genie then vanished,
He would no longer be his slave.
Soon the man realised his stupidity
For he was still trapped in the cave.

He now owned all he had wanted,
Everything riches and power could bring,
But trapped without his freedom
They could be of no use to him.

Later the headlines would read
Around the world from end to end:
"Richest, most famous man's grieving wife
Is to inherit money and marry his friend."

Lamb Lump

Mary had a little lamb,
It was famous for miles around;
She fed it only on beefburgers
So it weighed five hundred pounds.

Dainty Doggie

My sister painted our dog's toes
A shocking shade of red,
Then put lipstick on its lips,
"Ooh, it's so cute!" she said.

But I think it looks scary
And it really worries me;
It looks just like Mrs. Price
From number twenty-three.

Food for Life

Alone in her room each night
She sits there counting,
She's had nothing to eat
But the calories are mounting.

She thinks she's so fat,
Bursting out at the seams
Because of her daily diet
Of stupid glossy magazines.

She lies about food
That has passed her lips,
Blind to her mirror reflection
Of her coat-hanger hips.

She's jealous of her friends,
She thinks they look great
But they are all like her,
Obsessed with their weight.

Her parents they worry
That she looks so thin;
She faints each day
But she won't give in.

She now has to learn
To enjoy food again,
Feed her mind and body
And ease her pain.

She talks to trained people
Who understand and care,
Some have even thought
The same way as her.

If this sounds familiar
You may need help, too,
But you need to speak out
For them to help you.

You could make a start,
Put the magazines in the bin;
Please believe me when I say
That people are dying to be thin.

Stank Yahou

Durde Vest - King's England's big cheese (he's a 280 lb Gorgonzola!)

Bendie Bunn - King's England's own Anne Robinson!

Lille Phlipnerd - King's England's answer to unemployment!

Thank you from Zeg Shawl - King's England's proof that you can teach a monkey to write!